About the Book

This is the story of Peter Parker — a boy who learned about jazz.

When Peter was very small, he hung a sign on his door which read: Music Is Being Made — Do Not Enter, and he played his trumpet alone. One day, when he was older, he heard some daring and different sounds coming from someplace near-by. Peter went to look around.

From that day, Peter experienced new feelings and ideas about music and his understanding of it began to grow. By the end of the story, Peter had changed that sign to read: Music Is Being Made — Come On In!

Coward-McCann, Inc.

New York

Journey into Jazz

by NAT HENTOFF

With drawings by

David Stone Martin

J
c 1

CL

This is the story of Peter Parker —
a boy who learned about jazz.

When he was still quite small, Peter Parker had strong musical feelings.

When his father sang, Peter moaned.

When his mother sang, Peter howled.

By the time he was five,
Peter had his own toy trumpet.

At six, he was given a phonograph that was as small and sturdy as he.

And at seven, a transistor radio was added to fill
a bit more of Peter's huge hunger for music.

Suddenly one day Peter Scotch-taped a bold sign outside the door of his room: MUSIC IS BEING MADE — DO NOT ENTER.

The door was then closed.

From that day on, the sign appeared and remained in place from four to six every afternoon. From behind the door, Peter's parents could hear the trumpet, or the phonograph playing Prokofiev, or the radio playing Rossini.

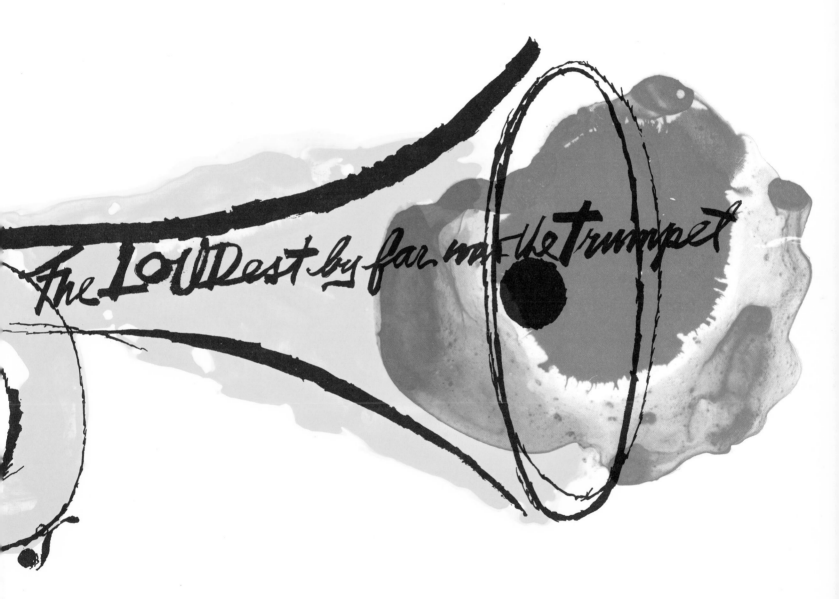

The LOUDest by far was the Trumpet

Soon Peter had a real trumpet and a real teacher, whose feelings about music were as strong as Peter's. From his room, Peter's parents began to hear scales. First, simple scales that soared slowly and floated back down again, sometimes stumbling on the way.

Then more and more difficult scales that climbed quickly and fell with dizzying speed.

From exercises, Peter went on to play real tunes —tunes that sometimes sounded like a small stream in a great hurry, or sometimes a deep and peaceful river, or a lightning storm, or sometimes nothing Peter's parents could imagine at all.

Peter told them that these last, strange sounds were called modern music.

They nodded, but were not quite sure they understood.

Soon Peter and his teacher began to play duets. Gradually it became difficult to tell Peter apart from his teacher.

By the time he was fourteen, Peter was a most accomplished and exceedingly proud trumpet player. There was hardly any music printed that he couldn't read.

One summer afternoon, although the sign was on Peter's door and he was undisturbed, he could not concentrate.

Somewhere, in some other house nearby, a small jazz band was playing.

Leading all the other instruments was a tenor saxophone player, who sounded more daring and more full of surprises than any musician Peter had ever heard. Peter was curious—and restless.

Peter took his trumpet, left his room, followed the sound, and discovered four young men in the garage of a house on the next block. Seeing his trumpet, the young musicians asked Peter to join them.

Peter looked, and looked again, but nowhere could he see any printed music.

He tried to join in their music, but something was terribly wrong.

Peter could not find a place for himself. Every time he tried, the music sputtered to a stop. He just didn't fit.

"Look, kid," the tenor sax man told him, "you know your way around that horn all right, but you don't know jazz. When you do, come back again. We'll be around."

Peter sadly trudged home. But he had been excited by the music he had heard in the garage.

So he began to listen to jazz records, especially records which featured trumpet players, and soon he was having fun trying to play some of his classical pieces in jazztime.

Peter also began to hear that each jazz trumpet player had his own way of playing.